A Living Testimony

Key Concepts in the Fight Against Cancer

BY REVEREND TYRONE CRIDER, SR.

CRIDER PUBLISHING, INC.
JANUARY, 2002

A LIVING TESTIMONY:
Key Concepts in the Fight Against Cancer
by Reverend Tyrone Crider, Sr.

Publisher
Crider Publishing, Inc.
3300 West 159th Street
Markham, IL 60426
(708) 557-1400

Cover design by Imani Graphics & Printing Services
Cover photograph by Paul Goosby

First Edition, Second Printing
ISBN Number: 0-9719790-0-6
Printed in the United States of America

All scriptures are taken from King James Version of the Holy Bible, except when designated.

DEDICATION

To my mother, Bernice Crider and my father, Lilton Crider
for training me up in the way that I should go.

To my spiritual father, Pastor Harry McNelty
for teaching me to trust in the Lord

To my wife, Regina,
for loving me back to life.

FOREWORD

If you're faced with a "GIANT" challenge that is
threatening to kill you, spiritually, physically or mentally, then I
urge you to grab hold of something solid. **A Living Testimony**
will take you on a journey that allows you to feel real life pain, real
life struggles, and true victory. Even as I re-lived the events of
this book, I cried, I laughed, and I rejoiced. If you need a faith
booster, or a trust activator, or a courage releaser, read this book
and discover the "I Am" God in every chapter.

-Regina Crider-

I Love you Tyrone Crider, Sr.

ACKNOWLEDGMENTS

First, I must give thanks and praise to God for healing my body and keeping me alive. To God be The Glory.

I thank Doc and Kris Rivers for opening up their home and their hearts and allowing me to spend quiet time in Orlando to lay the foundation for my book.

I thank my mother-in-law, Ms. Delois Williamson for keeping the kids while Regina and I worked night and day.

I thank Walter and Lynne Turner for their friendship and support in all of our endeavors.

I thank Herb Jackson, an awesome writer, for encouraging me to write my story.

I thank Tashieka Williams of *Make No Mistakes* for her excellent editing ability.

I thank my business partners for working around my schedule and continuously supporting me in this effort.

I thank Damita Jefferson of *Imani Graphics and Printing Services* for using her "gift" to design the back cover and for hangin' with us as much as she could.

I must give a very special word of thanks to Angela Hayes, CEO of *Imani Graphics and Printing Services* for having a patient, encouraging and supportive spirit. She endured the extra long nights and early mornings as she typed and designed every page of this book.

Angela, because of your faith, commitment, humility and sacrifice, God will continue to bless you and *Imani*. God has a great future for *Imani* and you have a significant role in building the Kingdom.

-Rev. Tyrone Crider

TABLE OF CONTENTS

CHAPTER

> *Yea, though I walk through the valley of the shadow of death, I will fear no evil: for thou art with me; thy rod and thy staff they comfort me.*
> *Psalm 23:4*

The Shadow of Death

Chapter 1

Sunday, March 29, 1998 is a day that I will always remember. I was serving as pastor of New Hope Community Baptist Church in Chicago, on the famous 47th Street. My sermon for that day was entitled "How to deal with Giant problems." I knew that this would be a memorable day because during the sermon, I had planned to tell my congregation that I had been diagnosed with lymphoma, cancer of the lymphatic system. Little did I know how memorable this day would be.

During my sermon, my wife, Regina, noticed that I was stumbling through my words. She recognized that I was having trouble seeing and reading the verses of the Bible. She noticed slurred speech, with hesitancy and uncertainty. As I came to the conclusion of my sermon, I asked the congregation to bow with me in prayer.

Regina did not bow her head.

Instead, she fixed her eyes on me because she knew something was wrong.

As the musicians played softly in the background, the head-bowed congregation waited for me to begin to talk to God. Halfway through the prayer, I began to sweat profusely. I paused...

My body began to slump forward over the podium. My thoughts went blank. I was losing consciousness fast. As I was falling to the floor, in a split second, Regina darted from the second row and caught me. She covered me and called out to me. Suddenly the church was out of control. The members were in a state of panic. In the midst of the commotion, the screaming and the shouting, I distinctly remember hearing my wife saying,

"Stay with me, Rev., stay with me."

The church members began to rush to the pulpit, the screaming intensified. Although chaos was at a peak, I was comforted and so thankful for the presence of my personal physician, Dr. Niva Lubin.

Two weeks prior to March 29th, I visited Dr. Lubin's office complaining about an earache and noting excessive fatigue. While examining me, Dr. Lubin noticed a lump behind my ear. She felt this was more than an average earache so she began to investigate my condition. Dr. Lubin ordered extensive lab work including several types of blood tests. Through intense investigation of the blood work, she discovered that I had a blood disease with the characteristics of Leukemia.

The blood tests signaled the presence of lymphoma.

Our plan was to introduce Dr. Lubin at the conclusion of my sermon to share with the congregation the details of my diagnosis. Dr. Lubin was seated next to Regina during the sermon and quickly made it to the pulpit to attend to me. As Regina comforted me, Dr. Lubin determined that I had regained consciousness. She gave Regina water for me and requested that a member call for an ambulance. Then, Dr. Lubin took the microphone and sought to calm the congregation by sharing the details of my diagnosis. After a few minutes, a medical team arrived from the fire station three blocks away and placed me in a wheel chair and rushed me to Mercy Hospital. Recognizing that I was headed for the hospital, *I came to myself.* I secretly asked a deacon to call my good friend Pastor Carl White, Jr. to tell him to come to the hospital to pray for me and to bring me some fried chicken!!!

In the emergency room, my sister, Wanda, paced the floor, while encouraging me. She and Regina comforted me while I was given an emergency blood transfusion. I remained at Mercy Hospital for three days under the watchful care of Dr. Lubin and a team of physicians that she recommended. After many more tests, it was confirmed that I had lymphoma. There were enlarged lymph nodes in my throat, my neck, my groin area, and my armpits. My blood counts were extremely high and my spleen was also enlarged. I had suffered significant weight loss and I continued to sweat profusely. Over the course of the hospital stay, I received several blood transfusions because the lymphoma caused me to become anemic.

That Sunday afternoon, as I lay in the bed in the hospital, I realized that I was in "the valley of the shadow of death." Lying there, my thoughts drifted toward my loving wife, my three daughters, and my four-month old baby boy, Tyrone Crider, Jr.

It was at that moment,
I decided to fight for my life.

In Sickness and In Health

Chapter 2

I met Regina Leslie in August of 1991.

I invited her and her 9-year-old daughter Shantoya (Precious) to the first worship service of New Hope on Sunday, November 3, 1991.

Precious remembered.

Regina and Precious did not attend the first worship service. Precious was very disappointed. Regina promised that they would attend our next worship service.

Sunday, November 3rd was another very significant day in my life. As I was preparing to deliver my first sermon as the founder and pastor of New Hope Community Baptist Church, I received a phone call from my sister, Wanda, informing me that my mother, Bernice Crider, died of liver cancer at 1:20 a.m. that morning.

Just before I preached that day, I sang mama's favorite song, "God Has Smiled on Me." I waited until it was time to preach to tell the congregation about my mother's death and then I preached with "a peace that passes all understanding." I found comfort in knowing that mama had gone to be with the Lord and that she had no more pain, sickness or sorrow. I preached her eulogy on Saturday, November 9th.

The next morning, Precious and Regina came to church. They sat in the second row in the auditorium of Martin Luther King High School where our services were being held. Precious was excited. She had never heard me speak. She had known me all of ten minutes in August...but she was excited to be at New Hope. I smiled at Precious from the pulpit, waving my hand to say hello. She and Regina returned my acknowledgement.

I invited Precious and Regina to our 6:00p.m. Inauguration and Dedication Service and to the reception at my home that evening. At the conclusion of the evening, I asked Regina to call me when they got home. Once they arrived home, Precious reminded Regina to call "Rev." That's when they realized that I had not given them a phone number. But leave it to Precious. She remembered that my roommate's name, Reginald Dixon, was on the doorbell in the hallway. Regina called information, obtained the number, and called me at home.

From that day, I loved Regina. I believed that she was sent to me from God. I believed that it was in divine order that she showed up the day after I buried my mother. For the next two years, Regina and I grew closer but I was afraid to commit to marriage. Organizing a church and becoming a pastor for the first time in my life was a lot of pressure. I was afraid to commit to marriage because I did not want to fail God, Regina or Precious. So, I did what I thought was right. I told Regina that I could not continue in a relationship with her because I did not know how to balance marriage and ministry.

She says, I kicked her to the curb.

What impressed me most about Regina was that after our relationship ended in 1992, she remained at New Hope. She continued in her pursuit to get to know God. She attended Bible study, sang in the choir, volunteered on Saturdays and didn't give me the time of day. She was on a mission to get closer to God. She loved worship. She loved praise. She loved learning the Word. But she never pursued me and she never pressured me to renew the relationship.

I must admit, I took notice of her growth. I also must admit that I missed her very much. I still loved her and I still believed that she was going to be my wife.

In March of 1994, I got sick and spent three days in the hospital. When I returned home, Regina came to see me. At that time, she let me know that she was making plans to marry her long-time friend, John. I was devastated by the news, but I didn't tell her. I asked if I could perform the wedding. She said "yes." We set the date for May.

To this day, I must thank my friends, Pastor White and Pastor Steve Jones because they urged me to tell Regina that I loved her and I wanted to marry her. One Friday night, we were having dinner and we began to discuss Regina's plan to marry John. They told me that I should not let her do it without telling her the truth about my feelings for her. The very next morning, Regina stopped by the office to pick up the Gospel Tribune to take it to the printer for me. I had a couple more pages to type before it could go to print. During her wait, she said to me, "Aren't you glad that I am marrying John? John is a very nice guy and you know he loves Precious and me." I told her that, as her pastor, I could not answer that question. She said, "Then don't answer it as my pastor, answer it as my ex and tell me how you really feel." I had no doubt in my heart that God brought us into each others lives to be mates, so I told her that I loved her and it was my desire to marry her. Regina decided to talk to John. They both agreed that even though they were best friends, getting married would not be the best thing for them. John and I talked man to man and went golfing the next week.

I promised Regina that I would marry her before the end of 1994. Although I waited until the last minute, I managed to keep my promise. On December 31, 1994 we got married. Pastor Clay Evans and Pastor Willie Jordan united us in holy matrimony.

I was excited about marriage. I was excited about Regina. I was excited about Precious. By this time, Precious was 13 years old; I was not sure how she would deal with a man in the home after thirteen years alone with her mom.

Well, God answered that question very quickly. Two months into our marriage, God sent Sandra Brown, an eighteen year old high school student, and her fourteen month old daughter, Felice, into our lives. When Sandy came to New Hope with her high school choir, she and two other friends joined the church during our Friday night fellowship. They returned Sunday for worship. Shortly after she became a member, we learned that she was without a home. One of her classmates asked if my wife and I could help. We couldn't find a home for her so she asked if she could stay with us for a weekend. I consulted my wife and she went into prayer. Before my wife could rise from her prayer, the Lord had given her an answer... *if she stays one night; she stays.* God did not give us a command. He gave us an option. We chose to let her and her daughter stay. That weekend lasted more than six years.

In December 1994, I was *Living Single* and in less than two months, I was *Married with Children* (three daughters and a wife).

Regina, Precious, Sandy and Felice were a joy to my life. I was a proud father of three girls. They were my children, sent to me from God. In November of 1997, God blessed us with a beautiful baby boy, Tyrone Crider, Jr. (T-man).

Four months after the birth of T-man, I was lying in the emergency room at Mercy hospital, holding on to life in "the valley of the shadow of death."

After the diagnosis, it was important for us to explain to our children the seriousness of my illness. We gathered the children together, and explained in detail what the doctors shared and what my options were. It was important that everyone understood how valuable teamwork and family support was at a time like this. We vowed to cooperate fully with one another in time, patience and love. Felice even agreed to help NaNa (Regina) take care of T-man. My mother-in-law, Delois Williamson, kept her door open as a 24-hour, on call, baby-sitting Grandma service. The girls quickly, and without resistance, stepped into their added responsibilities and the power of agreement was released in our home. I was comforted knowing that my home was flowing with peace and that made it easier for me to channel my thoughts properly and *focus on my healing*. That night we prayed together, hoping, believing and trusting God.

God had prepared Regina for such a time as this. She grew in her knowledge of the word of God. She became the "prayer warrior" in our home. Her hunger and thirst to know God had been rewarded. She had a "direct line" to God. She was truly an intercessor for our church and family. She believed God for my healing. She travailed day and night for my healing. I am alive today because God sent me an intercessor, a Christian companion, someone who loved the Lord and me, a supportive wife, and an angel who promised to be with me "in sickness and in health."

Concept #1: Family Support

A Soul Sister

Chapter 3

I was raised in a loving, supportive Christian family.
My sister, Wanda, and I have been close all our lives.
She was born December 27, 1957 and I was born
January 6, 1959. We had two older sisters, Lolita and
Darlene and one older brother, John. Although we
were 13 months apart in birth, it seems like we were
connected from the soul. Wanda was my sister in the
struggles of life and our bond was never broken
despite the trials and tragedies that life offered.
Together, we helped each other through the storms.

My maternal grandparents, Walter and Quinella
Hathaway were the second African-American family
to move to Maywood, Illinois, a western suburb of
Chicago. At age 8, my paternal grandfather, Mr.
Hugh Crider, died in his sleep, while visiting our
home and sleeping in my bed. My maternal grandfather,
Walter Hathaway, died when I was 14, after a series of
strokes.

Soon death made its way into our immediate
household. When I was 16, my father, Lilton Crider,
called me into his room and told me to "take care of

my mother and sisters." Fifteen minutes later, he died of lung cancer.

Our family has faced death many times. We remained strong in our faith and supportive of one another. In 1985, my sister, Lolita, was killed in a car crash as the police were chasing a drunk driver. She was 29 years old and the mother of two children, Nikkia and Ronnie, Jr. (Magic). In 1988 my mother, Bernice, was diagnosed with liver cancer. She remained strong until her death in 1991.

When our sister was killed, Wanda immediately adjusted her life to help mom raise Nikkia. Magic moved to Florida with his father. When mom died, Wanda assumed complete responsibility for Nikkia and raised her as well as her own son, Andre. In 1996, Nikkia graduated from Grambling State University. This was one of the great acts of love that my sister continually shows for her family. She is always willing to sacrifice her own agenda for others.

Wanda was the glue that kept me connected to my relatives. We stayed in contact by phone every day. As I traveled in the 1980s, she kept me posted on issues concerning the family. It is a blessing to have someone that keeps me connected and informed. That's my sister Wanda. Whenever I traveled, upon my return home, Wanda and I would reunite quickly and visit other family members together. Most of the time she would pick me up at the airport and my family update would begin. When we organized New Hope Church, Wanda quit her job to join me and to help organize our ministry.

As much as she respected me for my ministry and my work, I want her to know that she was the role model because of her consistent support and most of all, her loving sacrifice.

When I was diagnosed with lymphoma, Wanda, stepped in again. She kept the extended family updated and the support came pouring in from near and far. Phone calls, cards, contributions and assistance. My family was always there for me. Wanda and I were always very close. Wanda was my cheerleader, my soul sister.

So, it was no surprise that Wanda was pacing the floor in Mercy Hospital on March 29, 1998. She was always with me. Within an hour, Wanda had informed my Aunt Betty, Aunt Gwen, Aunt Colleen and Aunt Esther that I was in the emergency room. Once you reach those four, the entire family will find out.

Throughout my ordeal with cancer, Wanda remained by my side. She was the pillar of our family.

Concept #1: Family Support

A Second Opinion

Chapter 4

Once again, I want to thank Dr. Lubin for her support during my illness. My insurance provider, Unitedhealthcare, supported me every step of the way.

Through research, counsel and conversations with others, we chose Dr. Harvey Golomb of the University of Chicago Hospital to guide me through the treatment process.

In our first meeting with Dr. Golomb, he introduced Dr. Stephanie Williams and Dr. Tomislav Dragovich as his assistants. Dr. Lubin attended the meeting.

Because Dr. Golomb was known and respected as one of the best oncologists in the nation, he was not able to attend each meeting to discuss my treatment options. Dr. Williams became my lead physician.

My nurse was Ms. Sylvia Watson. When Sylvia took my initial blood test, she whispered these words to me:

"You can beat this."

The blood tests and x-rays showed that the cancer was very aggressive. The doctors recommended high dosage chemotherapy or radiation followed by a stem cell transplant.

Regina and I decided to get a second opinion.

The doctors also recommended that I should not preach for awhile. They thought it would be best to preserve my strength and prepare for treatment. At that suggestion, I asked Elder Wyatt Rush, a friend who supported New Hope from the beginning, to handle the preaching and pastoral duties of New Hope. This allowed me to *focus on my healing.*

As the days went by, more and more people began to hear about my collapse and subsequent diagnosis of lymphoma. One day my phone rang and it was Rev. Jesse Jackson. I had worked for Rev. Jackson since 1981, during my senior year at Morehouse College. We met when he was on a speaking tour promoting voter registration in 1980. I attended The National March on Washington that he organized in May of 1980. I was invited to speak at the rally because I was president of the student government association at Morehouse.

Rev. Jackson hired me in 1981 to become the National Youth Director of his PUSH for Excellence Program. For the next ten years, I traveled with Rev. Jackson serving in his 1984 and 1988 campaigns for President of the United States. In 1990, I became National Executive Director of Operation PUSH. I served in this capacity until the Lord led me to organize New Hope Church in November of 1991.

I was very happy to hear from Rev. Jackson. After working with him and understanding his vision for the people, I grew to love him. I believe, even today, that I gave him the best of the prime years of my life. I used my gifts and talents to promote his vision for a better world. In return, I obtained invaluable knowledge as I spent ten years with this great civil and human rights leader. I was given the opportunity to travel throughout this nation and around the world and to experience many different cultures and walks of life. My compassion for people deepened and my concern for social justice and economic equality heightened.

During the phone call, Rev. Jackson invited me to attend the Saturday morning broadcast of PUSH and he asked me if there was anything that he could do to help. I shared with him that I was seeking to get the best medical advice available and to learn about all of the treatment options. *I wanted a second opinion.*

That Saturday, Regina and I attended the broadcast of PUSH. We were warmly received as Rev. Jackson shared my situation with the PUSH family. After the meeting, we stopped by his office and he shared with me that he could get me an appointment to see his doctor at Mayo Clinic in Rochester, Minnesota. Regina and I were very excited about the possibility of going to Mayo Clinic because our research had shown that Mayo Clinic was one of the top medical facilities for cancer treatment. On Monday, we received a call from Rev. Jackson's secretary stating that his doctor had agreed to see me. Regina placed the call and scheduled the appointment.

The following week, Regina and I boarded a plane to Rochester, Minnesota. Our appointment was scheduled for Tuesday afternoon, however, we chose to go a day in advance so that I could relax mentally and physically. Again, I thank God for family support. My mother-in law was taking good care of our baby boy, and our girls were responsible enough to take care of themselves.

Mental peace is very important during any test.

Tuesday morning I was excited. I felt like I was about to receive the best care from the best doctors and that lifted my spirit. Regina did not show as much excitement. She simply supported my excitement by flashing an occasional smile and shaking her head from side to side. Instead, she was in a meticulous mindset. She had her notebook ready. She had her list of questions prepared. She was ready to hear and record every detail of the plan suggested for my total recovery.

My initial visit with Dr. Thomas Habermann was very interesting. While we were waiting for him to come into his office, we decided to analyze what kind of person he might be, according to his office decor. The plaques, pictures, poems, and drawings by children that dressed his office led us to believe that he was a man of compassion and positive mentality. Dr. Habermann was a very soft spoken physician. His manner of questioning was more personable than strictly professional. He listened very carefully to our responses. He was very comforting and patient. He was careful to choose encouraging words, but, at the same time, he was very precise and direct. He knew that I was a minister, so he encouraged me to activate my faith during the treatment process.

For the next two days, Regina and I waited for the test results. We rested and relaxed in the hotel. When I could, we walked around and did some window shopping. We took in a movie and enjoyed dinner together. It felt so good to have someone with me during this process. She made everything so comfortable.

When we returned to the room on Thursday, we received word that my results were in and I was scheduled to see Dr. Habermann the next morning. I didn't sleep much that night. Regina held me all night with words of reassurance.

As we entered Dr. Habermann's office, he seemed sad. He did not take a long time to share the news. The words he shared still ring in my mind today. He said, "What you have is a very aggressive cancer. It is nothing to play with or waste time on. *Based upon what we see, you have less than one year to live.*"

The room was silent. My mind was racing. Regina gripped my hand very tightly.

I asked Dr. Habermann, "What are my options?" He responded by saying, "I know you do not want chemotherapy. But because this cancer changes the cells so rapidly and so aggressively, at this point, I suggest chemotherapy at the University of Chicago. But it is up to you." As a man of faith he said, "Activate your faith, because faith without works is dead."

Regina said, "We've got to do it, we have to take the chemotherapy treatments."

When he said "Faith without works is dead", Regina knew that we did not have time to struggle with fear.

As we left the office and walked the long hallways to the hotel, we determined in our hearts to fight the death angel with all that we had.

When we returned to the room, we began holding each other on the bed and crying continuously through the night. Neither pride nor shame had any place in that moment. We needed to let go of our individual strength, break together, and let God renew our strength together.

At that moment, we truly became inseparable.

Concept #2: Supportive Medical Team

Knowledge Is Power

Chapter 5

My encounter with cancer taught me the importance and significance of early detection. From this experience, I learned that the diagnosis of cancer does not mean death. Many cancers are both treatable and beatable. I encourage everyone to make an appointment with your family physician and schedule annual or semi-annual screenings for the presence of cancer. If you are able to detect the signs and symptoms of cancer in the early stages it increases the possibility of overcoming the cancer.

Now that I know the symptoms of lymphoma, I realize that they were present in 1997. I remember an incident in November of that year, when my wife was pregnant, I was experiencing significant fatigue. As a matter of fact, it was exhaustion. I was invited to deliver a speech at Southern Illinois University in Carbondale. I knew that I was unable to drive because of fatigue. So, the University made flight arrangements for me but I was still too exhausted to get out of bed.

Regina and I attributed my fatigue to the fact that she was pregnant with our baby boy. Often times, I would share with friends that "we" were pregnant. We thought that I was experiencing "shared pregnancy symptoms."

We had no idea that it was the early symptoms of lymphoma.

When I was diagnosed with lymphoma, Regina and I began to study about cancer. Each day, we did a lot of research by searching the internet, reading books and asking questions of doctors and individuals who had encounters with cancer. One of the best books that we came across was the *MERCK Manual of Medical Information*. We called it "the red book."

Each night, we would read the red book searching for more information on different kinds of cancers, symptoms and treatment options. Regina was determined to know all that she could about lymphoma. She began to prepare a series of questions for the doctors. Her notebook was filled with new medical terminology. The doctors were impressed with her questions and inquiries regarding treatment and side effects. *It is very important for the cancer patient to have someone with them to ask the questions, record the answers and seek clarification.* My wife kept a notebook throughout the process. That kind of commitment gave me a strong sense of security in knowing that she was not going to miss a beat in gathering information and getting an understanding.

From our research and discussions with the doctors, we knew that we had a chance to beat lymphoma.

Many times when cancer is diagnosed people move into a state of panic. Fear sets in and the worst is expected.

Once again, it is important to remember and believe that the diagnosis of cancer does not mean death. Early detection increases the possibility and probability of survival.

It was the detailed examination by Dr. Lubin that detected the possibility of cancer in my lymphatic system.

Concept #3: Early Detection

I want to take a moment to recommend a list of symptoms and some screenings that can lead to early detection of some cancers

CANCER	SYMPTOMS	SCREENING
LUNG	persistent cough, spitting up blood	Chest X-ray
COLON	painful bowel movements, tumor, feces streaked with blood	Rectal Exam Stool Test
PROSTATE	difficult to urinate, frequent urination	PSA test Rectal Exam
BREAST	lump that feels distinctively different from breast tissue	Mammogram Breast Self-exam
LIVER	abdominal pain, jaundice (yellowing) fever, liver enlargement	X-ray
CERVICAL	recurring, abnormal bleeding	Pap smear Pelvic exam
STOMACH	Loss of appetite, loss of weight, anemia, blood in stool	CBC(Complete Blood Cou Stool Test
LYMPHOMA	enlarged lymph nodes, fatigue, enlarged spleen, night sweats, anemia	Blood Test X-ray

Symptoms are very indefinite, and they vary with each individual, please consult your physician regularly for positive diagnosis.

The Race for Life

Chapter 6

After meeting with the medical doctors. Regina and I decided to prepare my body for chemotherapy.

One of the calls that I received during the early days of my illness was from Martin Luther King, III. We were classmates at Morehouse College and we have remained close since I left Atlanta. Martin had a friend named Phil Oliver who worked for the Center for Disease Control in Atlanta.

Phil was a promoter of and believer in natural healing and alternative medicine. Every time I went to Atlanta, I would leave with copies of the newest information in the area of nutrition and alternative medicine. Phil would lecture Martin and me about our weight gain and challenge us to give serious thought to what we put in our bodies. We listened intently to Phil while we sat at the drive-thru window waiting for our bucket of fried chicken with fries and extra biscuits.

Well, when Martin called, he connected Phil and I on a conference call. Phil asked about 20 questions concerning my diagnosis. Because Phil was not in favor of chemotherapy and was knowledgeable in the area of nutrition, he quickly gained Regina's attention.

Therefore, Regina and I began to read a book entitled *Nutritional Healing*. Daily, we would read about the role of nutrition in healing and alternative options to chemotherapy. Through our research, we learned about Dr. Asari Hapi' who was located in Chicago and an expert in nutrition and alternative medicine. We shared with Dr. Lubin that we were going to make an appointment to see Dr. Hapi'. Once again, she supported our decision to consider all options.

Our visit to Dr. Hapi' was so enlightening. His conversation covered the role of medicine, nutrition, diet, psychology, environment and religion in the healing of the body. We shared with Dr. Hapi' our decision to take chemotherapy treatments. He did not discourage chemotherapy, instead he encouraged us to take the time to prepare my body for it. He recommended that we follow a specific diet and nutritional regiment to detoxify my body and build up my system for the negative effects of chemotherapy treatments. I agreed to follow his guidance. Regina decided that she would follow the exact same regiment in hopes that it would encourage me. It did.

My wife ate the same foods recommended for me and prepared and drank the same nutritional drink that was recommended. Some of the ingredients in the drink were spiru-tein, blackstrap molasses, spirulina and soy milk.

We faithfully followed the nutritional path set by Dr. Hapi'. Each day, I felt better and stronger but I did not gain any weight, and my spleen was still enlarged. To enhance this good feeling and prolong my strength, Dr. Hapi' treated me with a few sessions of acupuncture and it worked, for a short period of time. By the way, my wife did the acupuncture too.

Concept #4: Diet & Nutrition

> *Confess your faults one to another, and pray one for another, that ye may be healed. The effectual fervent prayer of a righteous man availeth much.*
> *James 5:16*

Prayer Meeting on 47th Street

Chapter 7

Since 1987, Pastor Richard P. Wilson of the Tried Stone Baptist Church in Detroit has truly been a great friend. We met when I was asked by Rev. Jesse Jackson to travel to his church and speak on behalf of Operation PUSH. Pastor Wilson was waiting in the airport to pick me up. I was traveling from Dayton, Ohio where I was serving as Director of Admissions at Central State University. Pastor Wilson and I never met in the airport. To this day, he says, "I was looking for *a black preacher* and I passed you up many times." Needless to say, I caught a cab to his church and we have been great friends since that day.

When Pastor Wilson heard the news of my collapse and my diagnosis of cancer, he did not hesitate to come. As a matter of fact, more than 175 members of Tried Stone came to Chicago. They came by bus, car and airplane. They brought the children's choir, the mass choir, the deacons, the ushers, the trustees, the associate ministers and any other members who wanted to attend.

It was such an awesome show of love. I cried as they filed into our church on 47th street. Pastor Wilson was nervous. No, he was scared. He had talked to Regina by phone but this was his first glimpse of the effect of the cancer on me. First, he noticed my significant weight loss of nearly 40 pounds. Then he noticed the enlarged lymph nodes. I pointed out to him the enlarged spleen and the lymph nodes in the arm pits. I also discussed the constant sweating, the fatigue, and the lack of breath.

He was devastated. He had come to encourage me and to be by my side. But this was too much for him. He saw death's hold on my body. He saw death winning this round. As we walked to the pulpit, he said, "Tyrone, I'm going to let the Holy Spirit lead me in this worship service. I'm not sure what's about to happen."

To say that worship in the African American church service is emotional is an understatement. On that day, on 47th street, our emotions climbed the scale. New Hope and Tried Stone came together to show their love for me and to encourage me in this fight. We were praising God through this storm, crying through this storm, hugging through this storm, and speaking victory through this storm.

The only challenge was that the *evidence* did not look good. My body was deteriorating right in front of my family, my church and my friends.

Despite that dilemma, I shall never forget the children's choir singing that Sunday morning. They sang "I Got to Tell it." The young soloist, Nikita

Hudson, could not stop singing, "I Got to Tell it." Facing the audience, she sang to every section. Then, she turned to the pulpit. She looked at me and Pastor Wilson and began to sing over and over, "I got to tell it, I got to tell it, I got to tell it." With tears rolling down her eyes she seemed to be telling me, "hold on, be strong, God will heal you."

With the congregation on their feet, Pastor Wilson took the microphone. As he began to speak, he said, "I will not be preaching today, the Holy Spirit has spoken. I am going to ask three members of Tried Stone and three members of New Hope to lead us in prayer and the final prayer will be given by Regina Crider and we will all attach our faith to her faith and believe God for the healing of my brother, Tyrone."

Our Sunday morning worship service had been turned into a prayer meeting on 47th street.

The first Tried Stone prayer was offered by Mother Clotile Carter, affectionately known as "Mom Carter." She adopted me as one of her sons in the ministry. The first New Hope prayer was offered by Venus Fitzpatrick, a faithful friend and prayer partner to my wife. The second Tried Stone prayer was given by Deacon Bernard Herbert, who offered me transportation whenever I was in Detroit. Then, from New Hope, Damita Harris, my wife's cousin and intercessor prayed for me. Finally, from Tried Stone, Mother Reamer Macklin prayed on my behalf. Then the microphone was given to my daughter, Sandy, who cried out in her prayer, "Oh Father God, please heal my daddy because *when I was a stranger, he took me in.*"

These individuals were carefully chosen because my wife was very particular about who she asked to pray for us during that time. She looked for saints who had the faith to believe God, courage before men and love for me.

It is wise to seek God's guidance when choosing your prayer warriors.

Finally, Regina began to pray. This was the altar call. Regina asked everyone who believed in the healing power of God to lift their hands toward me. For the next ten minutes, Regina began to talk to God on my behalf. She thanked God for bringing me into her life because, through my style of teaching, her hunger and thirst for the knowledge of God was rekindled. Then she simply began to pray "the word of God." She prayed every healing scripture that she had studied and everything that the Holy Spirit was leading her to say. My wife understood that nothing was more powerful than God's own word. She trusted wholeheartedly in Isaiah 55:11:

> *So shall my word be that goeth forth out of my mouth: it shall not return unto me void, but it shall accomplish that which I please, and it shall prosper in the thing whereto I sent it.*

The awesome and anointing power of God was present in the sanctuary.

> *What a friend we have in Jesus, all our sins and griefs to bear, what a privilege it is to carry, everything to God in prayer.*

Concept #5: Intercessory Prayer

> *I call heaven and earth to record this day against you, that*
> *I have set before you life and death, blessing and cursing:*
> *therefore choose life, that both thou and thy seed may live.*
> *Deuteronomy 30:19*

A Reason to Live

Chapter 8

In November of 1977, I was "called" to preach. In May of 1978, I delivered my first sermon. I will always honor the man who laid the spiritual foundation for my ministry.

His name is Pastor Harry McNelty.

The loss of my grandfathers and my earthly father helped me to develop a closer relationship with my Heavenly Father. Through their deaths, I found new life. From that point in my life, I put total trust in God. I accepted Jesus Christ as my Lord and Savior and began a new walk with God. I joined First Baptist Church of Melrose Park, Illinois and began my Christian walk under the teaching of Pastor McNelty. I shall never forget the lessons I learned under this great man of God. My grandfathers and my father were very significant men in my life. God used Pastor McNelty to fill the void in my life when my father figures passed away.

Pastor McNelty was a man who trusted God. He was not "ashamed of the Gospel." He preached with power, boldness, courage and compassion. As a young minister, I marveled at his complete faith in God. He truly believed that "God could do anything but fail." He poured this faith into me during my years under his teaching. He also believed that the church should do all that it could to meet the needs of the congregation and the community. Pastor McNelty was active in education, economic development, as well as, political and social activities. In his 42 years as pastor, he built an elementary school and a high school. He is the man who taught me about the role of the church in the revival of the community. He taught me to trust in the Lord. *As I was completing this book, Pastor McNelty died on December 25, 2001.*

As a young minister, I knew the hand of God was on my life. In 1977, I was trying to choose a college to attend. That year, I was named to the Illinois High School Basketball Hall of Fame in the Class A Division. I was recruited by Jerry Sloan, currently coach of the Utah Jazz and a former NBA All-Star with the Chicago Bulls. He offered me a scholarship to play basketball for a university in Indiana. But I also had a desire to attend Morehouse College in Atlanta, Georgia. Morehouse was the alma mater of Rev. Dr. Martin Luther King, Jr. and I learned about his ministry from Pastor McNelty.

Well, God helped me make the decision. Over the summer, Jerry Sloan was offered the head coaching position for the Chicago Bulls. He accepted and I chose Morehouse. In November of that same year, a plane crashed. On the plane was the basketball team from Evansville, Indiana University. Everyone on the plane was killed. From this experience, God introduced himself as the one who would order my steps and direct my path. I had a reason to live.

Trust in the Lord, with all thine heart
Lean not to thine own understanding,
In all thy ways, acknowledge Him
and He shall direct thy path.
Proverbs 3:5-6

Before I was diagnosed with lymphoma, Pastor Wilson had scheduled me to preach at his youth leadership conference at COBO Hall in Detroit, Michigan. Because of the cancer, he told me that I did not have to attend, if I didn't feel up to it.

But, I wanted to go! The initial "shock" of the diagnosis was over. I needed to take the two day trip to spend some private time with God. This would be my first opportunity to preach since I had collapsed. Pastor Wilson has invited me to preach to his youth every year since 1987. He knew that I had a heart for youth and I did not want to miss this opportunity to talk with young people about how to persevere through a trial. He knew that I had a passion to reach out to young people and encourage them to excel against the odds.

But he also knew that I could only attend with my wife's permission. As hard as it was for her to consent, she knew how much I needed some private time with God.

Pastor Wilson promised her that I would have a nurse and two young men to assist me.

I arrived early and rested the entire day so that I would have enough energy for the speech. Around 4:00p.m. one of my Morehouse classmates, Pastor Kenneth Flowers, came to my room to pray for me and he brought his anointing oil. Rev. Flowers is the pastor of the Greater New Mt. Moriah Baptist Church in Detroit, where I am frequently scheduled to preach for his youth revival. He prayed for me and anointed me with oil, asking God to heal my body.

As the time came for my speech, Pastor Wilson arrived with the assistants that he had promised Regina. They were gracious enough to let me remain in the room until it was time for the speech so that I would not have to endure two hours of sitting at the banquet.

As I walked into COBO Hall, I was acknowledged by the Master of Ceremonies. I received a heartwarming round of applause, it was an emotional moment. I wondered, would this be the last time, could this be the last time I would see my buddy Pastor Wilson? It brought tears to my eyes.

I walked slowly to my seat on the platform. I wished Regina was there. As I sat there, my mind reflected on the thousands of kids that God had allowed me to speak to in Detroit and around the nation. A collage of pastors crossed my mind as I thought about churches who had opened their pulpits to my ministry. As I sat there I knew that I could not let this disease win. I could not allow my body to succumb to cancer. I had a reason to live. I had to continue my ministry. I had to reach more youth. I had to preach more sermons. I had to turn this test into a testimony. I had to provide for my family. I had promised Regina that we would be together for a long, long, long, long time. I had to see T-man through college.

God showed me that night in Detroit that I had a reason to live. He let me know that my preaching days were not over.

As Pastor Wilson introduced me, he shared my story and he told the audience that this was my first sermon since I collapsed. I slowly stood to share my message. I thanked Pastor Wilson and Detroit for inviting me. I spent most of my twenty minutes talking to the youth about overcoming odds and encouraging the community to become more active in the lives of young people. As I came to my conclusion, it was very obvious that I was tiring. I held on to the podium, as I felt the shortness of breath. I concluded my sermon with some words that I had spoken at more than 107 colleges and universities during motivational speeches. Now, more than ever, I needed to "hear" these words for myself. They are called the ABC's of Life.

Concept #6: Sense of Purpose

ABC'S OF LIFE

Accept your challenge
Believe in yourself
Combine your words with action
Dedicate your life to your dreams
Expect some hard times
Fight on, be faithful, finish your course
Get God on your side
Have a made up mind
Inspire someone else
Journey with Jesus by your side
Keep on, keepin' on
Let love be the light to show the way
Make every day count
Never give up
Overcome your obstacles
Put your best foot forward
Quit quitting
Run the race with patience
Stand strong
Trust in the Lord
Use your talents
Value your time
Work until your work is done
X-ray your own lifestyle
Yearn to achieve all the goals you seek
Zealously strive to reach your peak.

© by Rev. Tyrone Crider, Sr.

Laughter is Good Medicine

Chapter 9

After my speech on Thursday, Pastor Wilson asked me to introduce Martin Luther King, III at the banquet on Friday evening. A great surprise for the kids happened when Tommy Ford from *The Martin Show* and Tiny Lister, who played "Debo" in the movie, *Friday*, decided to attend the Friday night banquet.

As Tommy and Tiny entered the room, Pastor Wilson was telling the audience that I was fighting cancer and that I had been given one year to live. Those words greatly affected Tommy Ford.

Later that evening, all of the speakers got together for fellowship at Fishbone restaurant. Through our conversation, Tommy and I learned a lot about each other. We learned that we were both recently married. His wife was named Gina. My wife was named Regina. His son, T. J. (Tommy, Jr.) was eight months old. My son, Tyrone, Jr. was six months old. He published a book using ABC's to reach youth. I had shared the ABC's of Life the day before. His desire was to motivate youth. My desire was to motivate youth. He loved God and golf and I loved God and golf. We decided to work together to achieve the goal of reaching young people. That day our friendship began. One month later, Tommy and Tiny came to Chicago to perform in a gospel stage play called *Perilous Times*. They decided to worship with me at New Hope on Father's Day.

Spending time with Tommy kept me in stitches. Even though I was fighting cancer, the laughter was very helpful to my state of mind. Tommy spent a lot of time in my home. He brought his family to Chicago to be with my family. We traveled to Miami to spend time with his family.

When I found the strength, Tommy and I would go to the golf course. That summer, we participated in some golf outings with Pastor White and Pastor Rush. There were times that I could not complete the round of golf but I still enjoyed being out there. We shared a lot of love and a lot of laughter. Tommy had a joke for every situation. He came to Chicago every month during my ordeal. I would set up meetings and speaking engagements for him and he would inspire kids. Then, we would golf, pick up some Kenny's Ribs and just chill. His presence in my life brought great joy to me, my family and many, many young people. The laughter was great medicine for me.

Concept #7: Freedom from Mental Stress

Simon Peter saith unto them, I go a fishing...
John 21:3a

Recreation Leads to Re-creation

Chapter 10

In the summer of 1992, Pastor Joe Ratliffe of the Brentwood Baptist Church in Houston, Texas was the guest lecturer at a conference hosted by The South Suburban Ministers Fellowship. During a session on church growth, he urged each pastor to find an interest, a sport or a hobby that would give them the opportunity to free their mind from the challenges of shepherding a flock.

He shared how time allotted for sport or recreation "refreshed" his mind. He told the group of pastors that "recreation leads to re-creation." These words blessed many of the pastors.

Today, a group of pastors go fishing on a weekly basis. Another group of pastors play basketball once or twice a week. I am in the group of pastors that decided to golf as much as we can.

For the patient with cancer or any serious illness, it is important to find or continue a hobby, sport or interest that relaxes or refreshes. **Inactivity can lead to the deterioration of the mind and body.**

During the spring and summer in Chicago, at least eight pastors gather together every Monday for a round of golf. We always play a minimum of 18 holes but we try to stretch it to 27. I look forward to seeing my crew on Monday morning. My crew includes Pastor Carl White, Pastor Wyatt Rush, Pastor William Jenkins, Bishop Tavis Grant, Pastor Samuel Hinkle, Pastor A. Edward Davis and Pastor Eddie Jenkins. We form two foursomes and have a great time. On Tuesdays and Thursdays, I play 9 holes with my buddy, Pastor Walter Turner at the beautiful, championship Odyssey golf course in the "cool of the evening."

When I was diagnosed with cancer, I chose to "continue living."

The diagnosis does not mean death. *Remaining active increases the possibility of remaining alive.*

It was very important for me to continue to golf. I was not always able to complete 18 holes. Sometimes, I couldn't finish 9. But I was active, alert, alive, getting fresh air, enjoying the fellowship of friends and continuing to *"live."*

Regina knew that I was in good hands with my golfing buddies. Pastor White and Pastor Rush had specific instructions to monitor my progress and they remained very conscious of my physical and mental state.

Regina has always been supportive of my desire to go golfing. She encourages me to golf because she knows that it relaxes me and refreshes my mind. I encourage her to go to the hair salon, to the spa for a massage and to the mall as much as she desires. Every now and then, she will join me on the golf course. In return, I would go to the mall with her. I would find a chair near the fitting room and while she shopped, I would make business calls so that I could pay for her merchandise. Because golf is a quiet game, I have to limit her time on the course because she screams too loud when she hits the ball.

My daughters are even worse. I only took Precious and Sandy to the golf course one time. On the second hole, a par 4, they came to the green arguing as to whether or not Sandy had hit her 18th or 19th stroke, because Precious was only on her 18th stroke.

Concept #7: Freedom From Mental Stress

> *A man that hath friends must shew himself friendly: and*
> *there is a friend that sticketh closer than a brother.*
> *Proverbs 18:24*

The Love Offering

Chapter 11

After much prayer and fasting, Regina and I decided to schedule the chemotherapy treatments. The treatment recommended by Dr. Williams was based upon a Houston model that had a 50% success rate. It was proposed that I take four sessions of chemotherapy as well as a stem cell transplant. The chemotherapy would be given intravenously. After each session, I would rest my body for two weeks.

As I was preparing to take the first session, I was in a state of contentment, trusting God and following the guidance of my doctors. Pastor Wilson walked into the room. His presence was comforting to me. It was nice of him to fly in to spend this day with me. At the end of his stay, Regina offered to take him to the airport. On the way to the airport, Regina and Pastor Wilson had a conversation concerning our financial stability.

Pastor Wilson was concerned about the state of our finances. He knew that cancer had taken away my ability to preach often and that was our main source of income for our family. He offered his assistance in raising some money to help us pay our bills. He suggested that we start a fund.

From that conversation, The Crider Fund was created. Pastor Wilson agreed to talk with other pastors to raise money to cover our expenses. He knew that removing financial stress would help me *focus* on my physical healing. What happened in the next two months blew our minds.

I asked Regina to call Pastor White and connect him with Pastor Wilson. Pastor Wilson and Pastor White jointly wrote and signed a letter to our friends around Chicago and throughout the nation. My sister, Wanda, opened a bank account in the name of The Crider Fund. Regina rented a post office box. Rev. Willie Barrow, Chairman of the Board of Operation PUSH joined the effort. She mailed out numerous letters and made many phone calls. The letter requested that each pastor contribute $200 to The Crider Fund. The goal was to raise enough funds to pay our mortgage and major bills for six months.

I have been preaching since May 17, 1978. God has allowed me to travel this nation and the world. Regina and I were able to prepare a list of pastors and churches that we felt would support The Crider Fund. Wanda organized the mailing list and letters were sent to the pastors.

During this time, my health began to get worse. The first session of chemotherapy had a dramatic affect on my physical body. I lost more weight. My hair began to fall out. My physical strength was waning. I slept about 18 hours a day. Regina and Wanda were with me every day. But through it all, the children remained strong, positive, and supportive. When all of my hair fell out, I started wearing a hat in the house. Precious and Sandy made me feel very good about myself. They told me I looked much younger.

Each day, the P. O. box was full of support letters and contributions. Apparently, pastors began to share with their churches that I was taking chemotherapy treatments and they wanted to be supportive of Regina and the family. The response was overwhelming!

Checks came in everyday from churches across Chicago and cities across the nation. I am especially grateful for the awesome show of love from the people of Chicago. Again, I do not want to risk omitting any person who contributed, so I am sending out a universal *"Thank You"* to all of you for your support. Listing each church that sent a contribution would be impossible. However, I would like to mention my pastor, Dr. Harry McNelty and his wife, Sister Edna McNelty, who raised $2,600. Pastor Kenneth Flowers, my classmate from Morehouse College, took up an offering in Detroit and sent a check from his church, Greater New Mount Moriah, for $3,000. Each day we received checks from Atlanta, Columbus, Louisville, Cleveland, Seattle, Dallas, Los Angeles, Indianapolis, Cincinnati, Miami, Detroit and many other cities.

I must share a special thank you with my sister-in-law, Jeryl Smith, who unselfishly gave us a love offering of $10,000 just a few months after losing her husband, Earl, to cancer. We were both in the hospital at the same time and our families were under an enormous amount of stress. I feel that what she did was a great act of love.

In Chicago, a benefit concert was planned for The Crider Fund. Pastor (now Bishop) Willie Jordan of St. Mark Baptist Church Cathedral held a gospel concert in my honor. The concert was scheduled just before my second session of chemotherapy.

Because of the significant weight loss, I did not have a suit that would fit. My suit size had dwindled from a size fifty-two to a forty-four. I was completely bald and self-conscious about my appearance. Regina went shopping and bought me a beautiful gold suit with gold shoes, with a matching black and gold koufee', an African style hat. She received a tremendous discount from our friends, Odie and Sharon Anderson, the owners of Unico Designs in Hillside, IL. I was shocked when I saw the suit. In addition to everything that was already going on inside, she wanted me to wear the brightest color suit I had ever worn in my life. My standard colors were black and blue. I must admit that Regina and the girls had a dramatic affect on my clothing selection. Let's just say they brightened up my wardrobe.

The concert at St. Mark was my first public appearance since the first chemotherapy session. I was very nervous. Many Chicago pastors showed their love and support by attending the concert and presenting their checks to The Crider Fund. The concert was awesome. It featured Lonnie Hunter and The Voices of St. Mark. Other special musical guests included Bryant Jones and Chosen, Chris Harris and the Fellowship of Friends and the Voices of New Hope.

As the concert came to a close, Pastor Willie Jordan called me to the pulpit for prayer. He allowed each pastor to share a comforting word and to present a check. A love offering was taken and $10,000 was raised that evening for my family and me.

Again, I cannot share everything that God allowed to take place through The Crider Fund. But I must say, although I am unable to mention every contribution, I thank God for every contributor.

Luke 6:38a says:

> *Give, and it shall be given unto you; good measure, pressed down, and shaken together, and running over, shall men give into your bosom...*

Concept #8: Freedom from Financial Stress

> *Finally, brethren whatsoever things are true, whatsoever things are honest, whatsoever things are just, whatsoever things are pure, whatsoever things are lovely, whatsoever things are of good report; If there be any virtue, and if there be any praise, think on these things.*
> *Philippians 4:8*

Think on These Things

Chapter 12

Because my father died of lung cancer and my mom died of liver cancer, I could have yielded to the temptation to "think" that I would die of cancer.

But I refused to "think" that.

The power of the mind is important in the fight against cancer or any serious illness.

In Proverbs 23:7, the scripture says,

> *"For as he thinketh in his heart (mind), so is he...."*

During my illness, I was determined to "think" that I would be healed. My constant refrain to myself and others was "this is a test that will lead to a testimony."

So many thoughts go through the mind when *cancer* is diagnosed. I had to remind myself that the diagnosis does not mean death. While many negative thoughts cross your mind, it is important to fight from within and counter those thoughts with scriptures and positive affirmations.

The healing process must include the mental and the spiritual realm.

In 2 Corinthians 10: 4-5, we read,

> *For the weapons of our warfare are not carnal, but mighty through God to the pulling down of strong holds; Casting down imaginations, and every high thing that exalted itself against the knowledge of God, and bringing into captivity every thought to the obedience of Christ;*

Although the diagnosis is negative, it is important to focus on the positive. It is important to fill idle time with positive activities, positive events, positive thoughts and positive memories. Cancer patients should try to surround themselves with positive people.

Because mom and dad died of cancer, I was often confronted with the thought that cancer was in my genes. My response to the discussion of "generational curses" or hereditary diseases is to stand on 2 Corinthians 5:17,

> *Therefore, if any man be in Christ, he is a new creature: old things are passed away; behold, all things are become new.*

Being in Christ gives you a *new bloodline.*

Fear and faith are exact opposites. Fear is the belief that the negative will happen in your life. Faith is the belief that the positive will happen in your life. F-E-A-R is False Expectations Appearing Real.

Studies show that people who have faith live longer, recover from illness faster, suffer less depression, enjoy better health and cope better with illness.

Therefore, the faithful must always remember 2 Timothy 1: 7,

For God hath not given us the spirit of fear; but of power, and of love, and of a sound mind.

Concept #9: Positive Affirmations

Speak your Healing

Chapter 13

In my senior year in high school in 1977, our basketball team at Walther Lutheran High School was faced with a difficult challenge. We were placed in the state tournament against the number one team in the State of Illinois Class A division, St. Michael Catholic School. There was only one person in all of Illinois who believed that we could beat St. Michael, her name was Bernice Crider.

My cousin Doc Rivers, coach of the Orlando Magic, and I still laugh at what my mom told me to do before the game. With Doc as my witness, mom said "Just go in that locker room and tell them you're going to beat them; and believe it!!!"

Needless to say, I didn't go into their locker room, but I did speak victory and I believed it. That game is cited as one of the highlights of Illinois high school basketball history. You see, we won the game by one point. St. Michael protested a call by one of the officials. The two teams went to court. The judge ordered that the second half must be replayed with no fans present. Guess what happened?

We won again by one point!

Still today, we marvel at the wisdom of the words of my mom. Speak your victory!!!

In January of 1996, Rev. Jamel Jackson, a former associate minister at New Hope Church, gave me a sermon on tape by Bishop T. D. Jakes. I had never heard of Bishop Jakes but this sermon was so powerful that I wanted to hear more. In the next eight months, I traveled to six cities to hear sermons and attend conferences where Bishop Jakes was speaking.

In that year I attended the Man Power Conference, The Singles Conference and even the Woman Thou Art Loosed Conference hosted by T. D. Jakes Ministries. I also traveled to hear Bishop Jakes speak at conferences hosted by The Full Gospel Baptist Church Fellowship in New Orleans, The Leadership Conference in Detroit, Michigan and at the Inauguration of Bishop T. Garrett Benjamin in Indianapolis. Even though each event was packed with thousands inside and out, I was able to get a seat because there was always reserved seating for clergy at each event.

I was so impressed and inspired by the teachings of Bishop Jakes that I set a goal to invite him to Chicago to speak for our organization, The Pastors Network. By attending six conferences in 1996, I became a familiar face in the clergy section, besides the fact that I was not hard to spot in a group of African-American clergy. Many times, I was invited to receptions for clergy with Bishop Jakes after the worship services. Each time, I would asked him to come to Chicago. At the final conference in Indianapolis, I got on the elevator with Bishop Jakes and he committed to come to Chicago for a two day conference in August of 1997.

The Pastors Network held the conference at The University of Illinois-Chicago Pavilion, which had a seating capacity of 9,000. For two days, more than 16,000 people heard the great messages of Bishop Jakes. About 500 people accepted Jesus Christ as their Lord and Savior and thousands renewed their commitment and grew in their walk with the Lord. During that year, I purchased more than 40 video tapes of sermons by Bishop Jakes.

Nightly, Regina and the girls would join me in the family room and we would watch a sermon by Bishop Jakes. We jokingly called those times "A Jakes A Day."

I am convinced that 1996 and 1997 were significant years in the spiritual growth of myself and my family as it relates to the healing and delivering power of God. The sermons strengthened us, empowered us, and prepared us for the fight with cancer.

Positive affirmations are very important for the patient with cancer. The Bible tells us in Proverbs 18:21,

Death and life are in the power of the tongue...

After the initial shock of the diagnosis of lymphoma, Regina and I began to speak healing, deliverance, and victory.

Our study of the healing ministry of Jesus, revealed to us that those who were healed had a role to play in their healing.

In Matthew 9:21, the woman with the issue of blood, after seeing many doctors,

> *said within herself, if I may touch but His garment, I shall be whole.*

When the centurion asked Jesus to heal his daughter, he said to Jesus in Matthew 8:8,

> *...speak the word only, and my servant shall be healed.*

Regina and I determined in our hearts to just speak the word of God, in Hebrews 4:12,

> *For the word of God is quick, and powerful, and sharper than any twoedged sword, piercing even to the dividing asunder of soul and spirit, and of the joints and marrow, and is a discerner of the thoughts and intents of the heart.*

I remember telling Wanda these words: **"This is only a test that will lead to a testimony."** I did not say those words because it sounded good, I said them because I believed them. I believed that God was going to use my fight with cancer so that I could be **"A Living Testimony"** of His healing power. So, I began to speak my healing and I spoke it every day.

Regina found her strength in the word of God. She called upon God every day. She began to speak both privately and publicly from Isaiah 54:17,

> *No weapon formed against thee shall prosper....*

We studied the word of God and we began to speak His word back to Him in our prayers. We stood on the precious promises of God and believed Isaiah 55:11,

> *So shall my word be that goeth forth out of my mouth: it shall not return unto me void, but it shall accomplish that which I please, and it shall prosper in the thing whereto I sent it.*

We believed what the prophet Isaiah said about Jesus in Isaiah 53:5,

> *But he was wounded for our transgressions, he was bruised for our iniquities: the chastisement of our peace; and with his stripes we are healed.*

Like Paul's account of Abraham's faith in Romans 4:20-21,

> *He staggered not at the promise of God through unbelief; but was strong in faith, giving glory to God; And being fully persuaded that, what he had promised, he was able also to perform.*

While we agreed to take chemotherapy, Regina and I were fighting the cancer with "spiritual therapy."

Speak your Healing.

HEALING SCRIPTURES

*No weapon that is formed against thee shall prosper; and every
tongue that shall rise against thee in judgment thou shalt
condemn. This is the heritage of the servants of the Lord,
and their righteousness is of me, saith the Lord*
Isaiah 54:17

*And said, If thou wilt diligently harken to the voice of the Lord
thy God, and wilt do that which is right in his sight, and wilt
give ear to his commandments, and keep all of his statues, I will
put none of these diseases upon thee, which I have brought upon
the Egyptians: for I am the Lord that healeth thee.*
Exodus 15:26

*And Jesus went about all Galilee, teaching in their
synagogues, and preaching the gospel of the kingdom and
healing all manner of sickness and all manner of disease
among the people.*
Matt 4:23

*Heal me, O Lord, and I shall be healed; save me,
and I shall be saved: for thou art my praise.*
Jeremiah 17:14

*And when he saw them, he said unto them, go show
yourselves unto the priests. And it came to pass,
that, as they went, they were cleansed.*
Luke 17:14

*For she said within herself, If I may but touch
his garment, I shall be whole.*
Matthew 9:21

Bless the Lord, O my soul, and forget not all his benefits: Who forgiveth all thine iniquities; who healeth all thy diseases;
Psalm 103:2-3

For I will restore health unto thee, and I will heal thee of thy wounds, saith the Lord;
Jeremiah 30:17a

He shall call upon me, and I will answer him: I will be with him in trouble; I will deliver him, and honour him. With long life will I satisfy him, and show him my salvation.
Psalm 91:15-16

Blessed is he who has regard for the weak; the Lord delivers him in times of trouble. The Lord will protect him and preserve his life; he will bless him in the land and not surrender him to the desire of his foes. The Lord will sustain him on his sickbed and restore him from his bed of illness.
Psalm 41:1-3 (NIV)

But my God shall supply all your need according to his riches in glory by Christ Jesus.
Philippians 4:19

But he was wounded for our transgressions, he was bruised for our iniquities; the chastisement of our peace was upon him; and with his stripes we are healed.
Isaiah 53:5

Concept #9: Positive Affirmations

Another Side of God

Chapter 14

Even though I had family support, a supportive medical team, freedom from mental and financial stress, and a sense of purpose and prayer warriors, the cancer still progressed and my body continued to deteriorate. Even though I *thought* healing and *spoke* healing, it seemed as if I was losing my fight against cancer. I continued to cry out to God. I really needed to see another side of the God that I loved and served.

From Genesis to Revelation we read the word "God" or "Lord" or "LORD God". Without the understanding of the original Hebrew text, we may miss the true meaning or character that is revealed in the use of that name.

Throughout the Bible, when "God" is mentioned it is important to note which name is given in the original Hebrew text because it helps to identify a specific characteristic of God. Let me give you an example. In the very first verse of the Bible, Genesis 1:1, we read: "In the beginning God created the heavens and the earth." In the Hebrew text, we would read, "In the beginning "Elohim" created the heavens and the earth. This is important because the name "Elohim" means "God alone is eternal." The name of God, "Elohim" lets us know that the "eternal" being created the heavens and the earth.

Okay, just one more example. In Genesis 22:7-8, God tells Abraham to take his son, Isaac to Mt. Moriah and sacrifice him as a burnt offering. On the way up the mountain, Isaac says to Abraham, "we have the wood and the rope, but where is the burnt offering?" Abraham responds by telling Isaac, "The God we serve will provide us a lamb." The name of God in the Hebrew text is "JEHOVAH-Jireh," which means "the Lord who provides." I have given two examples of names of God that introduce a characteristic or "side" of God. This was very important to me in my ordeal with cancer because I needed to see another side of God.

I already believed God to be "Elohim" or eternal. All my life God has been "JEHOVAH-Jireh", my provider. But I needed to see another side of God. I know God as "El-Shaddai" or all-powerful. Through my tithe, I acknowledge God as "Adonai", the owner of everything. But I needed to see another side of God. I teach people that God is Yahweh or JEHOVAH meaning "I AM that I AM". As a matter of fact, I have lessons on the names of God that include:

JEHOVAH-Nissi	"The Lord is my Banner"
JEHOVAH-Mekadesh	"The Lord who Sanctifies you"
JEHOVAH-Shalom	"The Lord is Peace"
JEHOVAH-Tsidkenu	"The Lord is our Righteousness"
JEHOVAH-Rohi	"The Lord is my Shepherd"
JEHOVAH-Shammah	"The Lord is There"

But I was fighting for my life. I was fighting against a disease that took my father and my mother. I was fighting against statistics, against facts, against negative reports, against probabilities, against the odds. And I needed to see another side of God!!!

The side of God that I was looking for, I found in Exodus 15:26. The Hebrew name for this side of God is"JEHOVAH-Rophe," *The God that heals.*

My encounter with cancer introduced me to JEHOVAH-Rophe, *the God that heals.* This is how God revealed this side of himself to me.

One morning, Regina received a call from Kathryn Rush, one of her prayer partners during this season. Kathryn stated that she had received a "prophetic word" from God concerning me. She told Regina that she had to speak this "word" to me first. I was not home at the time. Regina gave Kathryn my cell phone number. Kathryn called me and shared the "word" from the Lord. I was overwhelmed by the "word" because it spoke to my hunger and desire to hear from God and to *"know"* this side of him. I asked Kathryn to call Regina back and tell her to type the "word" from the Lord. This is the "word" that Kathryn shared with me on that day:

I am Jehovah your God.
You will go into that land of promise.
I go before you as a consuming fire,
lighting your path and destroying your enemies.
Destroying that which is not of me;
that sickness, that disease.
This sickness is not unto death.
But that my glory might be revealed.
By my son's stripes you are healed.
And they shall know that I am the one who sent thee.
Hold Fast. Let no man steal thy crown.

Regina typed this "word" out and then she passed it out to our prayer partners and asked them to pray this "word" daily and to believe God for my healing. She posted this "word" on the wall inside my hospital room and on the wall of our bedroom. She also kept it in the briefcase that she carried. She was literally and spiritually holding fast to this "word" from the Lord.

Another account of God speaking to us came during my first session of chemotherapy session. God also spoke specifically to my wife.

According to Regina:
My husband was sleeping. The chemotherapy was being given intravenously. We were on the first bag. I kept watching him. I kept watching the faint move of his body. I needed to do something to help him but there was nothing physically that I could do. I read scripture. I kissed his face a million times. Every time he opened his eyes, I flashed a happy face. But inside I was falling apart. I was breaking. Suddenly, I felt something stirring deep on the inside of me that I had never felt before. The stronger this feeling got the

more nervous and frightened I became. I did not know what to make of it.

The time was about midnight. We were fortunate to get the same nurse again tonight as we had last night. She was familiar with how protective I was of my husband. She saw the prophetic word that I taped upon the wall. She had seen and heard me singing and reading and praying to my husband. When I told her I needed to go home for a few hours, I could sense that she would monitor him very closely for me and that I could trust her care of him. I told her to call me immediately if he woke up. While I was driving home, I started telling God how afraid I was for my husband. How I could feel his fear. Lord, what can I do to help him? He has to live!! Lord you said in Psalm 91: 14-16:

Because he loves me, I will rescue him; I will protect him, for he acknowledges my name. He will call upon me and I will answer him; I will be with him in trouble, I will deliver him and honor him. With long life will I satisfy him and show him my salvation.

When I did that something happened in me. That feeling that I was so confused about earlier, didn't confuse me anymore. I knew that what I had said, had a direct effect on the shift in my spirit. When I got home, I went into the bedroom and fell on my face. I began to pray with a fervency that I had never known. I called out as many scriptures as I could think of. Then I settled down. Face down on the floor, I couldn't move. The house was totally silent. No one was there but me. But I heard a voice. I began to respond to the voice almost robotically. I reached for some oil that Pastor Jones had given me and I began to *anoint my body* in all of the areas that the doctor had identified tumors in my husband's body. These were the words of my prayer to God: "Lord, my lymphatic system is healthy. My husband's is not. Let me share my healthy system with my husband. Lord, we are one. Everything that affects him affects me and since we are one, please heal my husband. "Lord, I believe and I won't doubt it. In Jesus' name, amen."

I stayed in that position until the phone rang at about 3:30am. It was Pastor Wilson, from Detroit. He said, "Baby, how's Tyrone, for real. Is he going to leave us, Gina?" I responded in anger. I said, very harshly, "NO!" I just anointed my body everywhere he has a tumor and I believe God is going to heal him!" He said, "I'm sorry baby, I'm scared. I love Tyrone and I don't want him to go nowhere. But, if you believe God is going to heal him, I do too."

And this is the confidence that we have in him, that, if we ask anything according to his will, he heareth us: And if we know that he hears us, whatsoever we ask, we know that we have the petitions that we desired of him.
1 John 5:14-15.

I knew that God would heal my husband because I acted according to the instructions of the Holy Spirit. My natural man would not have anointed my body. But my spirit man knew to anoint my body. My natural man would not have acted out of faith but my spirit man knew that faith was the key to our victory. *Hallelujah!! Glory to God!!*

After this, Regina put a sign on the outside of the door to my room that simply read:

IF YOU DOUBT, STAY OUT!!!

Concept #10: Faith in God

A Place Called Victory

Chapter 15

159th street in Markham, Illinois is a very special place for me. The offices of The Pastors Network and The Gospel Tribune Magazine are located on 159th street. The headquarters for my "personal" State Representative Harold Murphy are on 159th street. I spend countless hours with Representative Murphy talking about the issues of life and developing strategies and programs that can make life better for people all over the world. Many of the programs that we offer in the community come directly from my conversations with Representative Murphy. He has been a "father figure" for me and he is the elder statesman in south suburban Cook County. I truly value the time I share with him and the knowledge and wisdom that he shares with me.

Two blocks away from Rep. Murphy's office is a place called Victory. At 2901 West 159th street in Markham, Illinois, God has placed Victory Christian Assembly Church where my friend, Rev., Dr. Carl L. White, Jr. serves as pastor.

I met Pastor White in 1990, when I was serving as

President of Operation PUSH. Pastor White was eating at Edna's soul-food restaurant on the west side of Chicago when I walked in. I introduced myself to him and asked him to join me in my efforts at PUSH. From that meeting, we became friends for life.

For more than 10 years, we've worked together fighting for justice and fairness in society. He was a pastor who believed that the church had to meet the needs of the "total man" if it were going to be effective. This belief drew me to Pastor White because I have always felt that the church must lead the way in the fight for liberation, equality, empowerment, justice, and fairness.

Pastor White was the best man at my wedding. He did a great job, even though he arrived at the wedding early and I was an hour late because he forgot to pick me up from my house.

During my fight with cancer, Victory was a prayer station. Because of my relationship with Pastor White, I knew he had someone praying for me constantly. I had gone through my first chemotherapy session and the evidence was very visible. Although it's what people expect, the side effects of chemotherapy are very hard to accept. It looked like I was losing the fight. I was losing my strength. I was losing weight. I was losing my hair. I was losing my ability to walk short distances. I was even losing my golf game. (oh no). From all indications, it looked like I was losing.

One day, during my second session of chemotherapy, my wife seriously needed a break. I'll let her tell you what took place.

According to Regina:
I was on my way home to freshen up. I thought to myself, maybe I'll even stop by mom's and spend an hour with her and the baby. I was in need of some motherly comfort and some baby magic. My mom kept our son day and night during this time. I would go to her house and spend a little time with T-man between my trips to and from the hospital.

On this particular day, I started out with home as my destination. The University of Chicago Hospital is located on 58th and Maryland. By the time I had gotten onto the Dan Ryan Expressway, approximately two miles from the hospital, I was crying severely for my husband. I had left him lying so still and breathing so shallow. The nurses convinced me that he was not in any pain and that the medicine would have him out for a few hours. They told me, "Now would be the best time for you to take a break."

As I was driving, I began to feel guilty that I had left without letting him know. I didn't want him to awaken and I not be there. I felt guilty because I knew that I needed to get away for a moment for my own sake. I felt guilty that I had not spent any quality time with my baby. I felt guilty that I had left the girls responsible for the daily operations of the house. The guilt demon was on my back and he was heavy. So I decided to call Pastor White to tell him how desperately I needed prayer. This call wasn't about my husband. *I needed prayer for the strength to make it through.* I was crying so hard that Pastor White could hardly understand what I was saying.

Realizing that I was at a breaking point, he said "Gina, come by the church now. Don't go home! Come to the sanctuary and let us pray for you and my brother."

It was such a relief to hear the tone of concern in his voice. I felt like I no longer had to be strong and save face. I could let go of my stubborn pride and not be embarrassed. I finally felt comfortable enough to lean on someone. When I got to Victory, Pastor White met me at the door and led me straight into the sanctuary. He instructed his administrative assistant, Sister Pamela Wright, Sister Deborah Turner and Sister Patricia Tatum to join us. He asked each person to pray in a specific order and he would offer the closing prayer. He placed me in the center. As the first prayer was offered, I sank to the floor weeping profusely. By the time we reached Pastor White for prayer, he was weeping harder than I. Everyone had kneeled to the floor, sobbing, praying and interceding.

I saw how hurt Pastor White was at the thought of what his friend was going through. So, I began to pray for him. God moved so mightily through our prayers that at the end of this experience, we were hugging and smiling and laughing. Our faith had been boosted and the joy of the Lord became our strength. My strength was renewed and I was ready to run and not get weary. I was reassured that my husband and I had true intercessors warring on our behalf. That alone gave me the strength to go on.

I'm so glad that I stopped by Victory; the place where battles are won.

Concept #10: Faith in God

Great Is Your Mercy Towards Me

Chapter 16

After the second session of chemotherapy, I continued
my weekly visits to the hospital for my blood test and
weigh in. My doctors had already scheduled the third
session of chemotherapy. But, I began to notice the
return of my hair. My weight began to climb and my
energy had increased dramatically. I was able to stay
awake most of the day, thinking, reading and even
typing on my computer.

Regina could see the changes as well.

Sylvia, my nurse, coordinated my weekly clinical
visits. Each week we would take the blood test, go to
lunch, then go home. She would call my home in the
afternoon to report the results.

My weight gain and high energy level encouraged me
but the weekly blood test did not show significant
change in my blood counts. My doctors still wanted
me to complete a third session of chemotherapy.
Regina and I decided to wait one more week.

As I prepared for my weekly blood test, Regina drove me to the hospital. Our spirits were high. We both felt that this report would be better. We followed our normal routine. Test, lunch, home, wait for the call from Sylvia.

For some reason Sylvia did not call until the next morning but we were not available. The results were recorded on voicemail. Three years later, we still listen to the original message left by Sylvia:

"Good morning, Reverend Crider.
Sylvia from the University of Chicago calling.
Your counts are fine.
WBC (White Blood Cells) 5.2
Hemoglobin   14.1
Humaticala   42.7
Platelet Count   210
All within normal ranges
Sodium is normal.
Potassium is normal.
Liver enzymes are normal.
Everything looks good.
Take care.
Talk with you later, Reverend Crider."

Regina and I screamed, and rejoiced in God. We spent the entire day praising God. I cried. She cried. We hugged and hugged and hugged some more. God had answered our prayers. The cancer was gone. My body was healed.

The following weeks, I took more tests just to confirm my healing. I remember leaving the hospital for the final time. I asked my wife to take me to the nearest Christian book store so that I could purchase a song that I heard on the radio. We stopped by Pentecostal Word Explosion Christian Bookstore on 79th Street and purchased this song by the Williams Brothers:

> *"I am a living testimony*
> *I coulda been dead and gone*
> *But Lord you let me live on*
> *I am a living testimony*
> *And I thank the Lord,*
> *I'm still alive!!!"*

Concept #10: Faith in God

> *But my God shall supply all your need according to His riches in glory by Christ Jesus.*
> *Philippians 4:19*

These 17 Words

Chapter 17

As I mentioned earlier in the book, Regina and I began to speak the word of God into our lives. During my ordeal with cancer, God revealed his healing power to me through these 17 words found in Philippians 4:19:

> **But my God shall supply all your need according to His riches in glory by Christ Jesus.**

These 17 words helped me prepare myself psychologically and spiritually in my fight with cancer. Let's take a look at these 17 words.

BUT
The first word in the text is the word **BUT**.

As you fight cancer or any obstacle, you must have the boldness to say, **BUT**. I'm not just referring to an illness. If God gives you a vision, you will run into obstacles, stumbling blocks and even people with negative thoughts or doubts about your ability to achieve your goal.

Do you have enough confidence in the One who gave you the vision? When God gives vision, he also makes provision for the vision to become a reality. The scripture says:

But thanks be to God who gives us the victory through Jesus Christ our Lord.

God does not just give vision, he gives victory. That's why you must have the boldness to say **BUT** in the midst of doubt or fear.

The facts say you can't do it.....**BUT**
The statistics say you can't do it....**BUT**
The tradition says you can't do it....**BUT**
The report says you have one year to live...**BUT**

The God I serve has the final word. We don't walk by facts...we walk by faith. The facts said that Abraham at one hundred and Sarah at seventy-five were too old to have a child......**BUT** they had a child.

The facts said that there was a Red Sea in front of the children of Israel.....**BUT** God parted the red sea.

The facts said that there was a wall around Jericho....**BUT** the walls came tumbling down.

The facts said Daniel was in the lions' den with hungry lions...**BUT** the lions didn't touch him.

The facts said that the King turned the fire up seven times hotter and threw the Hebrew boys in....**BUT** God took the heat out of that fire and even walked in the furnace with them.

Wow...Isn't that encouraging to know that God will not only take the heat out of the fire **BUT** He will get in there with you!!!

Can you say **BUT** regardless of the facts, regardless of the statistics, regardless of the opinions of others, regardless of how things look, regardless of doubt and fear?

Yes, I was given one year to live in 1998.....**BUT** my confidence, trust and faith was in God.

MY GOD
The next two words in the text are **MY GOD**.

These two words symbolize the fact that we must have **a personal relationship** with God. Paul says, **my God.**

In your battle with cancer or any other obstacle, you must have a personal relationship with God. I am not talking about a religion. I'm talking about a relationship. I'm not talking about a routine, I'm talking about a relationship. God wants a personal relationship with you.

Religion will make you sing in the choir...Relationship will make you sing in the car.

Religion will make you pray at the altar on Sunday only...Relationship causes you to talk to God anywhere.

God wants to walk with you and talk with you every day.

Paul says **"my God."** Paul is not the only one who emphasizes a personal relationship. One of the most famous passages of the Bible is a model for the development of a personal relationship with God. Let's look at the 23rd Psalm. David emphasizes a personal relationship with God:

*The Lord is **MY** Shepherd; I shall not want.*
*He maketh **ME** to lie down in green pastures:*
*He leadeth **ME** beside the still waters.*
*He restoreth **MY** soul: He leadeth **ME** in the paths*
of righteousness for His name's sake.
*Yea, though **I** walk through the valley*
of the shadow of death,
*I will fear no evil: For Thou art with **ME**;*
*Thy rod and Thy staff they comfort **ME**.*
*Thou preparest a table before **ME** in the presence*
*of **MINE** enemies: Thou anointest **MY** head with oil;*
***MY** cup runneth over.*
*Surely goodness and mercy shall follow **ME***
*all the days of **MY** life:*
*And **I** will dwell in the house of the Lord for ever.*

My personal relationship with God helped me defeat cancer.

SHALL
The next word in the text is **SHALL**.

The word **SHALL** symbolizes the promises of God. Every believer should get excited when they see the word **SHALL** because it is usually connected with a promise from God. When we accept Jesus Christ as our Lord and Savior, we become a King's Kid. Therefore, we inherit the precious promises that God made to the family of the faithful.

Look at these words in Romans 4:20-21

And Abraham staggered not at the promise of God through unbelief... and being not weak in faith, he believed everything that God had promised He was able also to perform.

Whew...do you believe that everything God has promised, He's able to perform?

I do and I did during my fight with cancer. When I see the word **SHALL**, I see a promise from God. There are more than 365 promises in the Bible (that's at least one for every day). Let's look at a few:

PROVERBS 3:5-6
Trust in the Lord, with all thine heart.
and lean not unto thine own understanding.
In all thy ways acknowledge Him, and
*He **SHALL** direct thy paths.*

ISAIAH 54:17
*No weapon that is formed against thee **SHALL** prosper;...*

PSALM 27: 1, 5
*The Lord is my light and my salvation; whom **SHALL** I fear?*
*The Lord is the strength of my life; of whom **SHALL** I be*
*afraid?... For in the time of trouble He **SHALL** hide me in his*
*pavilion: in the secret of His tabernacle **SHALL** he hide me;*
*he **SHALL** set me up upon a rock.*

ISAIAH 40:31
*But they that wait upon the Lord **SHALL** renew their strength;*
*they **SHALL** mount up with wings as eagles; they **SHALL** run*
*and not be weary; and they **SHALL** walk, and not faint.*

In the midst of your trial, stand on the promises of God and he **SHALL** deliver you.

SUPPLY ALL YOUR NEED

The next four words in the text are **SUPPLY ALL YOUR NEED.**

The four words symbolize God's awesome ability to meet every need that you have. The key word in this group is ALL. Not some of your need...**ALL of your NEED.**

When I was growing up in Maywood, Pastor McNelty had the congregation read Matthew 6:25,33. A very familiar text in the Baptist tradition:

> *Therefore, I say unto you, take no thought for your life, what ye shall eat or, what ye shall drink; nor yet for your body, what ye shall put on....But seek ye first the kingdom of God, and His righteousness; and all these things shall be added unto you.*

Take no thought for your **life** represents your **future.**
What ye shall **eat** represents **food.**
What ye shall **drink** represents **fountain.**
What ye shall **put on** represents **fashion.**

Matthew was letting us know that God will supply all your need.

In **Isaiah 52:12**, we read these words:

> *For ye shall not go out in haste, nor go by flight:*
> *For the Lord will go before you; and the God of Israel will*
> *be your rereward.*

When I was a young minister, I used to think that rereward was a typographical error in the Bible. But through my studies, I learned that rereward means "rear guard." Now, it makes sense to me and comforts me in knowing that God will "go before me" and be my "rear guard."

Isn't it good to know that God's "got your back"?

Finally, in Exodus 3, there is a conversation going on between God and Moses. God is telling Moses to go and tell Pharaoh to let his people go. Moses responds to God by asking this question, Whom shall I say sent me? What a profound question. This question forces God to come up with a definition of Himself. God answers Moses' question with a definition of Himself that *defines* who He is but does not *confine* who He is!!!

He tells Moses, **"I AM THAT I AM."**

The key word in God's answer to Moses is **THAT**.....

In essence, God is saying,
If you need a DELIVERER, I am **THAT**...
If you need a COMFORTER, I am **THAT**
If you need a SAVIOR, I am **THAT**
If you need a FRIEND, I am **THAT**
If you need a HEALER, I am **THAT**

This is why the Apostle Paul could boldly say, **SUPPLY ALL YOUR NEED.**

ACCORDING TO HIS RICHES IN GLORY
The next six words in the text are **"ACCORDING TO**

HIS RICHES IN GLORY."

These six words tell us HOW God will supply all our need. He will do it "**according to...**"

Stay with me, now.

You are looking for healing. You are looking for a new job. You are looking for victory. HOW will God meet this need?   The answer is: **"according to His riches in glory."**

Okay let's talk about this. I still think you have some questions.

What are riches in glory? Is my new job in glory? Is my healing in glory? Is my new car or house in glory? **NO!!!**

Let's look at some of God's *riches in glory.*
One of his *riches in glory* is called **GRACE**.
Another of his *riches in glory* is called **MERCY**.
Yet another of his *riches in glory* is called **FAVOR**.

When God decides to meet our need, based upon the actions of our faith, He dispatches His riches to work on our behalf. Let me give you an example:

In Luke 17:11-19, we read about ten lepers who asked Jesus to heal them. In verse 13, the lepers cry out, "Jesus, Master have mercy on us." They wanted to be cleansed but in their request they mentioned one of **"His riches in glory."**

In verse 14, Jesus' response to their request is "go show yourselves unto the priest." And then the text says "as they went, they were cleansed."

The lepers desired to be cleansed. Jesus responded with an ASSIGNMENT...something for them to DO. Faith without Works is dead.

Jesus said, "Go." Start walking. Move out.
The lepers could have questioned this assignment (leaned to their own understanding) because the priests were the ones who sent the lepers to live outside the city.

But instead, they walked by faith. And as they started walking...God dispatched His MERCY and they were cleansed. Please note that their request was granted *after* they started walking.

Too often, we make a request to God and then sit there and wait for a blessing. Look at the word **ASK**. It is spelled **A-S-K**. In those three letters are the key to getting your prayers answered:

Ask and it shall be given
Seek and ye shall find
Knock and the door shall be opened.

After you **ASK**, get up off of your knees and "go get your blessing."

If you want a job, **ASK** and then fill out as many applications, as you can. If you want a new home, apply for a mortgage. Don't let your credit report stop you from applying. If you don't apply you don't give

God an opportunity to dispatch GRACE, MERCY or FAVOR.

If you never show up, you don't give God the opportunity to show out. *Go for it.*

I knew that chemotherapy was a risk. But I had to *go* get my healing.

BY CHRIST JESUS
The final three words of the text are **BY CHRIST JESUS.**

Nothing in the previous fourteen words can be achieved without the final three words, **BY CHRIST JESUS.** In John 15:5, Jesus says, "...Without me ye can do nothing." In Philippians 4:13, Paul says, "I can do all things through Christ which strengthens me."

The words **BY CHRIST JESUS** symbolize the need for **AUTHORITY.**

My checks are not acceptable without an authorized signature.

My credit purchases cannot be approved without verification of my **NAME** and signature.

In the Christian faith, Jesus is the Authorizing Agent.

Jesus says:

I am the way, the truth, and the life: no man
comes to the Father, but by me.
John 14:6

And if ye abide in me and my words abide in you, ye shall ask what ye will, and it shall be done unto you.
John 15:7

The role of Jesus in the Godhead is described for us in John 1:1-4 (NIV):

In the beginning was the Word, and the Word was with God, and the Word was God. He was with God in the beginning. Through Him all things were made; without him nothing was made that has been made. In Him was life, and that life was the light of men.

In 1 Corinthians 15:57, Paul talks about the need to go to God through Jesus Christ when he says:

But thanks be to God which gives us the victory through Jesus Christ our Lord.

God honors the name of Jesus as "the name above every name." Paul writes in Philippians 2:9-11:

Wherefore God hath highly exalted him, and given him a name which is above every name: That at the name of Jesus every knee should bow, of things in heaven, and things in earth, and things under the earth; And that every tongue should confess that Jesus Christ is Lord, to the glory of God the Father.

As a believer in the power of the name of Jesus, when cancer came into my body, I prayed boldly and with confidence because the Bible says:

And this is the confidence that we have in Him, that, if we ask any thing according to his will, He heareth us: And if we know that he hear us, whatsoever we ask, we know that we have the petitions that we desired of him.
(1 John 5: 14-15).

As a resident of Chicago, I was spoiled during the six championship years of the Chicago Bulls. The Michael Jordan years in Chicago were thrilling days in our town.

We were the Champions. We knew it. We believed it. Each year we expected it.

I also want to thank the major advertisers of that era, McDonald's, NIKE, Gatorade and Coca-Cola. I want to thank them because their sponsorship of the NBA games allowed millions to see the victories by the Bulls.

I remember the announcers saying: "This game has been brought to you by the following advertisers."

As I think about my fight with cancer, I can thank many people for their support during my illness, but I am A LIVING TESTIMONY and my healing from cancer was *brought to me:*

BY CHRIST JESUS

Thank you for reading our book!

Ti'Ana Denice Crider
Born: September 28, 2000

Contact Information

Rev. Tyrone & Regina Crider
Crider II Ministries

P.O. Box 2026
Country Club Hills, IL 60426

708-957-9840 office
708-957-9806 fax

tycrider@aol.com
ginacrider@msn.com